# Frightful Fiends

Edited By Holly Sheppard

First published in Great Britain in 2020 by:

Young Writers
Remus House
Coltsfoot Drive
Peterborough
PE2 9BF
Telephone: 01733 890066
Website: www.youngwriters.co.uk

Printed and bound in the UK by BookPrintingUK
Website: www.bookprintinguk.com
YB0427M

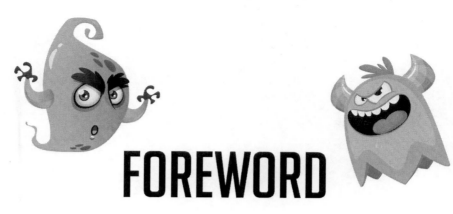

# FOREWORD

Hello Reader!

For our latest poetry competition we sent out funky and vibrant worksheets for primary school pupils to fill in and create their very own poem about fiendish fiends and crazy creatures. I got to read them and guess what? They were **roarsome**!

The pupils were able to read our example poems and use the fun-filled free resources to help bring their imaginations to life, and the result is pages **oozing** with exciting poetic tales. From friendly monsters to mean monsters, from bumps in the night to **rip-roaring** adventures, these pupils have excelled themselves, and now have the joy of seeing their work in print!

Here at Young Writers we love nothing more than poetry and creativity. We aim to encourage children to put pen to paper to inspire a love of the written word and explore their own unique worlds of creativity. We'd like to congratulate all of the aspiring authors that have created this book of **monstrous mayhem** and we know that these poems will be enjoyed for years to come. So, dive on in and submerge yourself in all things furry and fearsome (and perhaps check under the bed!).

# CONTENTS

## Intack Primary School, Blackburn

| | |
|---|---|
| Harrison Hale (9) | 58 |
| Lucas Walton (9) | 59 |
| Ethan Hazlett (10) | 60 |
| Umar Ismail Kanmi (9) | 61 |
| Bushra Hafiz (9) | 62 |

## Lewis Street Primary School, Eccles

| | |
|---|---|
| Bamo Amin (10) | 63 |

## Loxford School, Ilford

| | |
|---|---|
| Alishba Rameez (10) | 64 |
| Sibel Hassan (7) | 67 |
| Ioana Daniela Craciun (9) | 68 |
| Glory'nn Helen Lartey (9) | 70 |
| Ayaat S Khan (7) | 72 |
| Hadjer Sarah Marmouze (10) | 74 |
| Dunstan Sodengbe (10) | 76 |
| Inayah Hoque (9) | 78 |
| Vinushika Chandragumar (10) | 80 |
| Bhavya M Patel (9) | 82 |
| Nailah Ansari (10) | 84 |
| Zaynah Malik (9) | 86 |
| Harrison Li (9) | 88 |
| Asmaa Sakkaf (10) | 90 |
| Ayaan Nasir (7) | 91 |
| Rushaanth Jeyakumar (7) | 92 |
| Ayesha Malik (9) | 93 |
| Azim Ahmed Ali (10) | 94 |
| Zahra Malik (7) | 95 |
| David Fowowe (10) | 96 |
| Simrah Ahmed (7) | 97 |
| Muhammad Abdullah Cheema (10) | 98 |
| Gwyneth Li (7) | 100 |
| Nidhirav Surendar (7) | 101 |
| Vihaan Parvatini (9) | 102 |
| Alayna Malik (8) | 103 |
| Tiana Satheeskaran (9) | 104 |
| Jalal Khan (9) | 105 |
| Ali Keita Mbalo (11) | 106 |
| Tanjil Islam (9) | 107 |
| Muhammad Eshan Kamran (9) | 108 |
| Zahra Khan (10) | 109 |
| Evelyn Bexigas Soares (8) | 110 |
| Aliza Jumah Ali (8) | 111 |
| Raynah Shukri (7) | 112 |
| Iman Majid (7) | 113 |
| Mahnoor Nisa Malik (9) | 114 |
| Alisha Majeed | 116 |
| Sumaiya Khan (9) | 117 |
| Shanti Panesar (9) | 118 |
| Kshaf Naqvi (9) | 119 |
| Isabel Garrouch Girón (8) | 120 |
| Iyaz Korim (9) | 121 |
| Daniya Ahmed (8) | 122 |
| Sharleez Ghouri (9) | 123 |
| Syon Danny Maisuria (10) | 124 |
| Sana Chithara (9) | 125 |
| Saarah Badawood (9) | 126 |
| Rahman Syed (10) | 127 |
| Nia Edo-Sarfo (10) | 128 |
| Ariana Gandacov (9) | 129 |
| Tasin Rashadul Huq (7) | 130 |
| Manveer Lota (10) | 131 |
| Aaminah Moosa (10) | 132 |
| Mustafa Ashraf (8) | 133 |
| Maryam Ali (8) | 134 |
| Faheem Ismail (9) | 135 |
| Zaina Munir (7) | 136 |
| Zain Khan (8) | 137 |
| Kisaa Naqvi (10) | 138 |
| Rayyan Rahman (8) | 139 |
| Kinza Naveed (9) | 140 |
| Rashvin Udawatte (10) | 141 |
| Aman Singh Bedi (9) | 142 |
| Safwan Khan (9) | 143 |
| Sheikh Monim (8) | 144 |
| Haleema Faisal (9) | 145 |
| Eshal Hassan (8) | 146 |
| Adan Uddin (10) | 147 |
| Nethwan Udawatte (8) | 148 |
| Zahra Esmaeili (8) | 149 |

| | | | |
|---|---|---|---|
| Huriyah Iqbal (8) | 150 | Jessica Merrick (8) | 193 |
| Rayan Khurram (8) | 151 | William Wallace (9) | 194 |
| Bani Kaur Bedi (8) | 152 | Mollie Johnson (8) | 196 |
| Syeda Hamnah Shah (7) | 153 | George Gostik (8) | 197 |
| Ismaeel Azhar Ashraf (9) | 154 | Ben Gregory (8) | 198 |
| Iman Choudhri (9) | 155 | Jonti Michael Drummond | 199 |
| Adyan Rahman (7) | 156 | Simpson (8) | |
| Sara Arif (7) | 157 | | |

Zain Butt (10) — 158

## Teignmouth Community School, Teignmouth

| | | | |
|---|---|---|---|
| Khadija Asghar (9) | 159 | | |
| Yasmin Mudhir Sharif (9) | 160 | Tillie Louise Gardener (10) | 200 |
| Hassan Jaferi (8) | 161 | Sophia Dalling (7) | 201 |
| Ibsham Ahmed (8) | 162 | Grace Swift (10) | 202 |
| Khadija Farhan Khan (7) | 163 | Laila Auckland Edwards (7) | 203 |
| Sunni White (9) | 164 | Alfie Morley (7) | 204 |
| Abdullah Khan (9) | 165 | | |

Yusuf Ahmed (8) — 166
Jannat Al-Zara Haq (10) — 167
Yusuf Aamir (7) — 168
Zara Sethi (7) — 169
Riam Parekh (9) — 170
Mathu Shalini (7) — 171
Mysha Miah (8) — 172
Roshan Jeyakumar (7) — 173
Mihran Khan (8) — 174
Zwabit Intesaar Hamid (8) — 175

## Salisbury Cathedral School, Salisbury

Tomisin Hannora Joel (8) — 176
Bertie Barrington (8) — 178
Jasper Sainsbury (9) — 180
Honour Veitch (8) — 181
Allegra Sturgeon (8) — 182
Tofunmi Joel (8) — 184
Emily Luton (9) — 185
Safiya Laycock-Wright (9) — 186
Beth Sainsbury (9) — 187
Robert Wallace (9) — 188
Amelia Parker (8) — 189
Noah Maguire (8) — 190
Henry Seaward Gower (8) — 191
Rachel Fisher (8) — 192

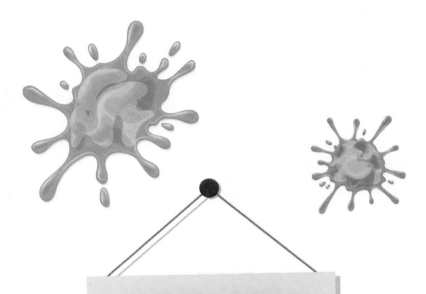

# THE POEMS

# Monsterville

Monsters, monsters
Stinky monsters
Old and creepy
Dark and gloomy
From short to tall
From stinky and smelly
From pretty and ugly
From gentle to brutal
This is the monster that I have made
At night he roams through the eerie night
Searching and searching for juicy children to eat
While you are sleeping
The brutal monster might be out there
Looking for you and your family
At night
This monster may look brutal and gentle
But this is my monster that I have made
So please respect my monster
Otherwise he may be looking for you at night.

**Ilyas Mahamed (9)**
Al Falah Primary School, Clapton

1

# The One-Eyed Monster

As I run through the hallway
I hear a monstrous creak
I panicked and really started to freak
"Who is that?" I asked
I stopped looking around the walls
And stared at a monster with one eye
I noticed that its other eye was closed
Because it was fried
I was face-to-face with an angry beast
He screamed, "Get out of here before I crunch you!"
I tried to hide but he roared at me
I then picked up my pace
And never went back to the ancient hallway.

## Muaad Hassan (9)
Al Falah Primary School, Clapton

# Shape-Shifter

He roars through the gazing sunlight
Waiting for children's laughter
Lurking in separate areas
Don't let him hear you
Or you'll end up in a trap
Or in the belly
As dark and scary as nightfall
Fangs as big as an elephant
As tall as a skyscraper
Beware of this shape-shifter
It's impossible to escape
So you better shut that mouth of yours
If you wake him
You'll never know where you'll end up
Beware of this shape-shifter!

**Abdullah Ahmed**
Al Falah Primary School, Clapton

# Slimacon!

I had no idea at first
Forget my hunger and thirst
I went over to my desk
Visible from all the rest
Was a creature with long hair
That made me stop and stare.

It looked like slime
But with a head
How divine
Had a glamorous sparkly horn
And big eyes.

My hand gradually reached over
It felt as soft and squishy as marshmallows
And as stretchy as Elastagirl
I decided to keep it forever
Be my best friend forever and ever.

**Zarah Vally Mamode (9)**
Al Falah Primary School, Clapton

# Sleepy Monster

He was sleeping
Snoring so loud
I could hear him from a cloud
The mountain crumbled to bits
Wow look at the crowd
They were proud
He woke up
He growled
Everybody ran as fast as they could
He stomped
He bumped into a lamp
*Boom!*
He hit the floor, made a huge mark
Everybody gasped
The cars were beeping
People were sleeping
Waking up not peacefully
But disturbed fully.

## Muawiyah Shah (9)
Al Falah Primary School, Clapton

# Anubis

Anubis, Anubis
That's his name
He knows his game
Also he feels no pain
He breaks, makes and takes life away
He makes things really pay off
He's not real but more as fiction
Maybe people should worry about non-fiction
He would make you die or even cry
But certain to fly and not to stand by.

## Faahim Abdiaziz (10)
Al Falah Primary School, Clapton

# Spooky Night

As I went to bed
I felt something under my bed
It was a monster
I didn't dare to look
So I grabbed a dagger
I thought maybe I should keep this next to me
Just in case it attacks me
But my dad woke me up
As soon as I woke up, I checked under my bed
It was just a dream.

## Zakariya Dahir (9)
Al Falah Primary School, Clapton

# Spiky Sam Wanders Around

This is Spiky Sam
Spiky Sam is as greedy as a lion
He roars like thunder
He is very slimy and ugly
Spiky Sam has saliva all over him
He is always messy and dirty
Spiky Sam looks so scary
Strange people get shocked
Because of his hairy body.

**Sumaya Omar (9)**
Al Falah Primary School, Clapton

# The Monster

Her eyes were red
She poisoned children with lead
They couldn't go to bed
The next day they would end up dead.

So say goodbye to your friend Ned
Because you don't know
Whether or not
She's under his bed.

## Tasniim Mohamed Osman (9)
Al Falah Primary School, Clapton

# Monster Friends

Monsters are friends
Rate them
In my world nobody's scared
You might think they are scary
Because they are big and hairy
But in my world
It's just me playing pool with my perfect monster
friends.

## Dawud Arefin (9)
Al Falah Primary School, Clapton

# Colourful Monster

I'm a red monster
With an orange face
I have yellow feet
And green legs
Blue ears
Purple heels
What else could I have?
A pink nose
So why don't you call me
The Rainbow Monster!

**Aliyah Hassan (9)**
Al Falah Primary School, Clapton

# The Monster Under My Bed

I can hear a growling under my bed
I can smell the bubbling red
I can feel the blue eyes keeping watch
I can taste the fear
But stood before me
He is called Spotty
I can hear me and Spotty giggling
I can smell the food he's eaten
From Mum's secret sweet tin
Too many sweets, he's wriggling
I can feel his soft blue fur
I can taste happiness in the air
As I laugh and sway
"You are a friendly monster,
You have caused quite the stir!"

**Robyn Bradley (9)**
Ballymagee Primary School, Bangor

# The Child Snatcher

Tiptoe down the echoey hall
Hope he doesn't hear you
Early in the morning
That's when he's out too.

You don't want to run into him
He's your worst nightmare
With his huge big flappy wigs
Soaring through the air.

If he snatches you
You won't come out alive
He's already caught some children
One, two, three, four, five.

**Mia Hegarty (9)**
Ballymagee Primary School, Bangor

# There's A Monster In My Wardrobe!

There's a monster in my wardrobe
At least five foot tall
If you see him
He'll make you fall!

There's a monster in my wardrobe
Be careful if you hear bangs
Because if you open your wardrobe
You might end up in his fangs!

There's a monster in my wardrobe
Very scary indeed
And he wonders who else
Is purple and blue.

**Erin McGrath (10)**
Ballymagee Primary School, Bangor

# Pete The Monster

My name is Pete
I have big feet
I have a big belly
That wobbles like jelly
I am soft and furry
But I do worry
That children are scared of me
My only plea
Is if I win
I will show you my grin.

**Lucy Violet Stewart (9)**
Ballymagee Primary School, Bangor

# Freaky Faye

Freaky Faye
How beautiful and grey
When the day turns to night
The monsters play
They do not have fun in the sun
And by day
Freaky Faye lies in bed.

## Faith Miller (10)
Ballymagee Primary School, Bangor

# The Friendly Monster

My monster is as big as a tree
His fingers have spikes
He's very friendly and nice
He sings a song for me at night
My big monster has a fluffy body
He wears clothes that are very spotty
His eyes look like coins
But his colour is like bubblegum
I love my big monster
Because when I need something from the tree
The monster picks me up to help me
When he sleeps his snores sound
Like my dad's old car
My monster friend has a big heart
And green hair like a forest
My monster's tongue is as long as a snake's
He loves eating a lot of cakes
His mouth is so big a whole person could fit inside
If I feel his tummy when his food is yummy
He is very scary and gets hairy
He's very fluffy because his body is puffy.

## Kamil Hawrysio (9)
Elstow School, Elstow

# Mirror Man

Hung low in the misty sky
A little boy entered
The trees drowned with happiness
All was dreary now.

Racing upstairs
The young measly soul
Lay low his secrets
We shall never know.

A thing ominously roams the mirror
A spine-chilling creature giving you a shock
A broad devilish smile, evident to your hopeless
eyes
Teeth like jagged rock.

With triumphant cackle
A melancholy music rings in your ears
Solemn voice surrounds me with echoes
Seeking out your most solemn dreams.

It's a superstition, it's an imagination
Manipulating your mind, you know it's not true

Shut your eyes, it's just a bias myth
You won't be him, he won't be you.

It's not the shadow lurking in the abyss scaring you
It's your own negative thoughts, staring back at
you!

## Abdullah Azhar Faisal-Yaqoob (10)

Elstow School, Elstow

# Ouch! It's Ozzy!

Ozzy the monster is a formidable beast
He's sneaky and freaky and will give you a fright
He'll leave you quivering in fear at the very least
You won't see him coming as he moves through
the night.

With giant mutant tentacles, slimy and dripping
He's short and snake-like and very mischievous
Spookily, his tentacles are wild and whipping
His elf-like ears are as sharp as a blade.

With four eyes he'll see you from all angles
His netted feet are sharp enough to blister your
skin
Naughtily, his electronic horns will spark your hair
in tangles
So if in bed, beware of Ozzy the formidable beast.

**Ollie Greig (10)**
Elstow School, Elstow

# Mind-Controlling Cameron

Don't ever tell a deceiving lie
Because that's when he starts to lose his swooshing mind
Especially in this sinister time
At first, a gentleman and an amiable creature you will see
But if you pull a falsehood
He may stab you with his blade-like knee
Sorry to scare you, he really could
Says my sister who faced him in the wood
As we approached him she started to whine
For she knew she had spoken a lie
With his mind he cast a spell
That did not end very well
While being choked, she cried and cried
Then moments later she sadly died
Now you know the hazardous story of the girl who lied!

**Alyssa Leigha Abbey (10)**
Elstow School, Elstow

# Crawling Creeper

Monsters crawling everywhere
Creepy-crawlies everywhere
Monsters speeding for food
Teeth as sharp as a knife
As fast as a flash of lightning
The sight of a monster
His spikes can make blood
His horns can make poison
And his claws can rip off a person's skin
When he hears thunder he goes hunting
For flesh and bones
He drinks blood for his own blood
He mostly comes out at night
The gleaming eyes gleam with blood and greed
He's strong enough to pick up a house with one
hand
He's a monster
He's a creep
He puts nightmares into people's dreams at night.

## Matas Stankevicius (7)

Elstow School, Elstow

# Horrid Hazza

Hungry Hazza the strong mechanical monster
Big, scary and shiny
He likes to eat
But beware of his teeth
He will eat you
Even though he is tiny
He'll send you creepy things
Stealing your stuff like a thief.

You won't see him coming
He's sneaky and sly
In the room at night he'll give you a fright
You won't see him coming
He'll eat all your pie
He'll sneak in your bed
Eating you with a big bite.

His six spooky eyes are very scary
His spiky claws will rip your bed
His sharp claws will leave marks on your head.

**Harry Greig (7)**
Elstow School, Elstow

# The Monster Who Lived In My Garden

I'm going to tell you about the monster who lived
in my garden
He smelled really bad
And didn't say pardon
His wonderful name was Toddy
And he had a very spotty body
I liked to play with him in the day
Especially in the month of May
He loved to watch me on the swing
And I adored the joy that we would bring
He liked to play with fashionable dolls
On his head he had a massive mole
He had thick fur all over himself
And he kept his dolls on a very large shelf
*Boom!* One day he disappeared
And never returned as I feared.

**Leah Champkin (10)**
Elstow School, Elstow

# Mr Spotty

Mr Spotty was very funny and kind
Mr Spotty loved to dance and jive
Mr Spotty was walking around
Because he was going to town
There he was at the pet shop
He bought a pet and he named it Jet Spot
He loved his pet
But sadly he had to take it to the vet
Mr Spotty was very happy
So he threw a dance party
Mr Spotty danced and jived
He loved his pet but he hated taking it to the vet
Mr Spotty was very tired
He went to bed
Good night Mr Spotty and little Jet Spot.

**Olivia Damiano (8)**
Elstow School, Elstow

# Mischief Bliz

In Tokyo City the sky darkened
As the other side of the Earth lightened
The two superheroes came to fight crime
One green alien loved eating lime
Even though the limes are sour
Bliz eats them every hour
Little Bliz is very cheeky
And his voice is very squeaky
Mischief Bliz is always eating his shoes
And he drinks water from the loo
Busy Bliz is always fun
Then he's sad when it's done
We love Bliz, we can't deny
He's an awesome little guy!

**Lilly Gauntlett (7)**
Elstow School, Elstow

# A Scary Friend

There once was a monster called Alie
Who had no friends
One day she went for a walk
With someone, she wanted to talk.

A monster went up to her
Alie got freaked out
The monster was tall and orange
And five eyes she had, as well as four arms.

The monster said, "My name is Tilly, don't be afraid of me!"
"My name is Alie," said Alie
They both smiled and walked away talking to each other
Both of them became best friends!

## Amelia Lis (9)
Elstow School, Elstow

# Boggy Billy

Boggy Billy goes under your doors
Leaving his slime trail on your floors
But don't look at him at night
He might give you quite a fright.

Boggy Billy, awake at night
His seventy-eight eyes sensitive to sunlight
His furry mould-covered teeth attract gone-off food
His table manners are quite rude.

All the bad things he might find
I really don't mind
Boggy Billy is my pet
Tomorrow he has to see the vet.

**Eva Ruggiero (10)**
Elstow School, Elstow

# My Monster

Monsters come out at night
And rest in the day
They are scary and spotty
Monsters are hairy and bold
Some are naughty and kind
Monsters are small and big
My monster hates children
Because of their screams
If he sees you
He will take you with him
He will steal your dreams
And turn them into nightmares
My monster is pretending to be kind
But he is creepy.

**Sara Anwar (6)**
Elstow School, Elstow

# Monsters

**M** y monster is fluffy and green
**O** ne eye on his head is the strangest thing
**N** ice and round like a bubble
**S** top, don't try to pop him, there'll be trouble
**T** ea and biscuits are his favourite snacks
**E** xcitedly he will eat the whole pack
**R** elaxing and resting is his favourite thing to do
**S** noozing at night until the day is new.

## Siena Colucci (6)
Elstow School, Elstow

# Monster Bath

I've never had such a strange bath time
Sinking deep in monster slime
Thick white gloop in my hair
I want to shout but I do not dare
I look around for somewhere to run
But all of a sudden my hair's in a bun
Even though I'm covered in bile
The monster does a good hairstyle
Blood on the wall from the big fat monster
Shining like a sunburnt lobster.

## Harry Johnson (8)
Elstow School, Elstow

# Friendly Monster!

I found a door in my room
I opened it up to see a huge furry monster in it
I screamed
The monster hushed me
I ran as fast as I could
But it turned out
It just wanted to be my friend
So she was my friend
Her name was Jade
So I played with her
Until she had to go
She said, "Goodbye,"
And I said, "Goodbye,"
Off she went.

**Kacey Blackwell (8)**
Elstow School, Elstow

# The Very Scary Monster

He roars through the night
And gives you a big fright
Oh, what a sight
I wonder if he will be back tonight?

He is orange and pink
And lets out a big stink
He is big and round
And he tries not to make a sound

The monster under my bed
Is here to stay
Until the middle of May
When he will go out of town
To find his scary crown.

**Kyra Fraser (7)**
Elstow School, Elstow

# The Monster And Child

There is a monster on the floor
On the floor
There is a monster on my bed
On my bed
There is a monster on my door
On my door
There is a monster on my cupboard
On my cupboard
There is a monster on my stairs
On my stairs
There is a monster running out the door
I am not afraid anymore.

## Samrutha Parthiparaj (6)
Elstow School, Elstow

# Spiky Bliby

Bliby the monster went to see a doctor
For his poorly leg
After he went to see the doctor
He bought a box of rotten eggs
And took them to Monster Greg
Who also had a poorly leg
They both ate the rotten eggs
Once they finished eating
They burped with an awful breath
Of rotten eggs.

**Nicoló Della Santa (7)**
Elstow School, Elstow

# My Monster

My monster is very friendly
He reads books and writes with me
He looks like a hairy green ball
He has got big eyes
He likes to jump up and down
When I am feeling sad, he makes me laugh
I am happy when he is with me
I know when I grow up he will leave
But I will have memories of him.

## Deividas Naujokas (7)
Elstow School, Elstow

# The Godzilla

Godzilla was sleeping
But he was very angry
That he was hearing noise
But he lives under the sea
So he can be close to the city
So when he gets mad he can destroy cities
But when he's done he can go to sleep.

## Kacper Baginski (9)
Elstow School, Elstow

# My Monster

My monster has three eyes
My monster likes mince pies
My monster goes for a run
My monster likes to have fun
My monster is big and hairy
But my monster isn't scary!

**Izzy Ruggiero (6)**
Elstow School, Elstow

# Ted With A Shed For A Head

There is a monster called Ted
Who has a mechanical head
He acts like a clown
But when he lies down
His big mouth turns into a shed!

**Tom Hayfield (9)**
Elstow School, Elstow

# The Fluffy Ball

I can hear growling from the hungry fluffy ball
I can smell the sweet sugar that the pink ball has
eaten
I can see the pink fluff
From when she goes under my bed
I can feel the smooth, sharp teeth
While I dangle my arm off the bed
I can taste the sugar from the fluff off the floor.

I can hear the rumbling of the pink ball's belly
I can smell the sweet cotton candy that she has
eaten
I can see the dark blue eyes that shine in the
moonlight
I can feel the soft fluff off the carpet
I can taste the sweet cotton candy from the edge
of my bed.

## Brooke Catherine Airey (8)
Giggleswick Primary School, Giggleswick

# Bobble

I can hear a monster giggling as loud as a hundred children
I can smell the cold air from his minty, ginormous mouth
I can feel his sloppy, large tongue licking my dark hand
I can taste the spiky hair tickling my throat
I can see his grey foot kicking me.

I can hear nails scratching the wooden planks under my bed
I can smell the veggie trumps he does
I can taste chicken hitting my tongue
Like he's trying to feed me
I can see poisonous snakes surrounding my bed
Arghhh!
I can feel long, sharp nails touching my back.

## Evie Worthington (8)
Giggleswick Primary School, Giggleswick

# Animan And The Movie

I can hear massive barks
I can see a long tail dangling from the roof
I can smell Pet Danda in the lounge
So I decide to pause the movie
I can taste dog slobber
Then I look in the kitchen
I look behind me
And see a weird thing with spiky butterfly wings
Pouncing on the telly
I can feel fluffy fur
Then he turns around
Sits on the sofa
And we watch the movie
I warn him that my sisters are asleep.

## Daniel Griffin (7)
Giggleswick Primary School, Giggleswick

# Easter Buttons

I can hear my monster trying to get in contact with me
I can see the flowery tail dragging across as it walks
I can smell the Daisy perfume that it puts on
I can feel its wrinkles coming down my back
I can taste the poison tail from her.

I can hear her whining for help
I can see her headband under the bed
I can smell her gruesome breath
I can feel her scaly tongue
I can taste the slimy snails in her hair.

## Grace Scott (8)
Giggleswick Primary School, Giggleswick

# The Dream Taker

I could hear growling in my garden
I could smell its rotting body like cow poo
I could see smoke coming out of his house like a bonfire
I could feel his scales like a chupacabra.

I could hear a deafening roar
I could smell dragon breath
I could see a red glowing fire
I could feel a bite
*Chomp!*

## Finlay Chapman (9)
Giggleswick Primary School, Giggleswick

# Jefry

I can see his claws reaching out from under the bed and then, *bang!*
I can smell something
I hear creaking in the woods
I can feel his scaly back like a snake
I can taste some gone-off cheese
I can see him in a bin
I can smell his massive burp
I can hear him scratching his back
I can taste his blood.

## John Perrings North (7)
Giggleswick Primary School, Giggleswick

# Clany The Monster

I can hear banging on my wall under my bed
I can smell beautiful chocolate
I can see him shining in the light
I can feel a bumpy mattress
I can taste sugar-like sweet, chocolate ice cream.

I can hear him crunching
I can smell his feet
I can see his spiky hair
I can feel the hair tickling on my feet!

## Rosie Garth (8)
Giggleswick Primary School, Giggleswick

# Stinky

I can hear horrible trumps
I can see his disorganised bag
I can smell rotten teeth
I can feel his slimy back
I can taste his bitter chocolate
I can hear him giggling under my bed
I can see his scaly skin
I can smell his breath
I can feel his scaly skin
I can taste his chocolatey breath.

## Oliver Charnley (8)
Giggleswick Primary School, Giggleswick

# Big Bob

I can hear his loud growls in my house
I can see him eating scraps in the bin
I can smell oily poop from him
I can taste slimy cheese
I can feel mouldy cheese.

I can smell him, like rotten cabbage
I can see his big, big nest
I can feel his scaly neck
I can taste slimy poop.

**Ben Brummitt (8)**
Giggleswick Primary School, Giggleswick

# Monster Chase

I can hear rattling on my door
I can see his big horns
I can smell his cakey breath
I can feel him scratching on my bed
I can taste fresh goats' milk.

I can hear him crawling
I can see a little arm
I can smell rotten food
I feel annoyed
I can taste chocolate.

**Elliott Rutter (8)**
Giggleswick Primary School, Giggleswick

# Mr Amo (The Mechanical Monster)

I can hear his engine, it is as loud as a plane
I can smell his oil
I can see his armour
I can feel people being hurt

I can feel him breaking the other ships nearby
I can smell his Spitfires
I can see him
I can feel his bullets
I can taste machine guns.

## Ben Tobias Lawson (8)

Giggleswick Primary School, Giggleswick

# The Gloogle Elf

I can hear him stomp
I can smell his aftershave
I can see his claret and blue scales
I can feel his furry soft skin
I can hear him roar
I can smell his fishy breath
I can see his red eyes glowing in the dark
I can feel his rough skin
I can taste his slime.

## Blake Hughes (8)
Giggleswick Primary School, Giggleswick

# The Durp Monster

I can hear him lurking around my room
He smells like thin air
I can see his shadow
I can feel him as cold as liquid nitrogen
He tastes like ice-cold water
I can hear him lurking in the kitchen
I can smell him
I can see him hiding
He tastes like cookies.

## William Bainbridge (8)
Giggleswick Primary School, Giggleswick

# Slimy

I can hear giggles
I can smell slime
I can see green slime
I can feel smooth horns
I can taste jelly
I can hear rattling in the bin
I can smell stinky trash
I can feel the slime.

## Charlie Richardson (7)
Giggleswick Primary School, Giggleswick

# Flames

I hear a rattling sound in a deep dark wood.

But when I came near to it,
The wood was full of flames
Then I saw a monster holding a match.

It came near me, growled and ran away!

**Douglas Alfie Oliver (7)**
Giggleswick Primary School, Giggleswick

# Crystal

I can hear crying all night long
Her beautiful singing is like a mermaid
Singing at sea
I can smell chocolate
I can see her nice white eyes
I can taste her chocolatey fingers.

**Lily Marsden-Mellin (7)**
Giggleswick Primary School, Giggleswick

# The Monster

I can hear weird noises under my bed
I can smell rotten cabbages
I can see a floating ghost
I can feel the slime running through me
I can taste disgusting food in my mouth.

**Jack Crisp (8)**
Giggleswick Primary School, Giggleswick

# Monster Soup

I can hear it growling
I can smell its breath
I can see the cupboard door rattling
I can feel fear up my spine
I can taste birthday cake.

**Henry Bainbridge (7)**
Giggleswick Primary School, Giggleswick

# The Haleman

There is a monster under my bed at night
I can smell the smelly slime seeping out
I can feel the beady eyes keeping watch
It likes to eat children
It is like a treat
His arms are humungous
Make sure he doesn't see you
Or he will gobble you up
I can see his antennae
He can take happiness away from you
He will only bring you madness
Make sure he doesn't see you
Or he will gobble you up like you're a sweet
So go to sleep or you will die!

## Harrison Hale (9)
Intack Primary School, Blackburn

# Who's Under Your Bed?

One scary, rainy night
I was going to sleep
I heard an ominous noise
It was coming from under my bed
I didn't have the guts to look under
I heard the creature say,
"I'm Googly, I will gobble you up
Like a pack of sweets!"
I fell down the stairs
Not feeling pain for some odd reason
I then woke up
Realising it was a dream
I went downstairs
The news said there was a creature on the loose
Called Googly.

**Lucas Walton (9)**
Intack Primary School, Blackburn

# Disturbing Craig

Craig is spiky
He's scary
He'll give you a fright
If you find him under your bed at night.

Craig sits under your bed at night
With his long, sharp, shining spikes
He pops up out from under you
You're about to scream
Until he says, "Hello, friend!"
Then you realise he's a friendly monster.

## Ethan Hazlett (10)
Intack Primary School, Blackburn

# Terrible Tim

There is a monster, as slimy as anything
As terrifying as a lion
And in the night
He will crawl up your window
And feast on your yummy flesh
Be aware
Close your window
He will crawl out from under your bed
And before you know
You will be dead.

## Umar Ismail Kanmi (9)
Intack Primary School, Blackburn

# Scary Lobster

Scary Lobster is as scary as a spider
He'll haunt your house
He'll eat any mouse
He'll gobble you
He'll send a shiver down your back.

Scary Lobster is the most scary monster of all
So watch out for Scary Lobster!

## Bushra Hafiz (9)
Intack Primary School, Blackburn

# My Monster

Have you heard about my monster Grendel
My monster loves to scare people
Even when he is evil
He likes climbing trees
But mostly he likes eating peas
He doesn't like the smell of fish
And he definitely doesn't do the dishes
He loves eating meat
And he has sharp feet.

**Bamo Amin (10)**
Lewis Street Primary School, Eccles

# Ripper – The Story Monster

As large as a Minotaur
Ripper loudly snores
While the glowing sun sets
The luminous moon rises.

Shadows emerge from the darkness
Dancing around helpless
Finally the fiction-eating monster
Awakes from his slumber.

Shivering in the spooky night
The withered leaves whisper in no light
His spiky, brown fur enveloped his book-like body.

This story monster loves a meal of fiction
But detests even the tiniest crumb of non-fiction
Oh the boring, complicated words
All those long, useless facts!

This beastly creature's jaws are as sharp as razors
Ready to rip and eat thousands of pages

Creeping near the tall bookshelf
The temptation to gobble the words is irresistible.

So what will he eat today?
A starter of C S Lewis, yes he may
Great stories full of friendship and adventure
Also packed with myths and magic.

For this wild beast's main,
Maybe J.K. Rowling's novels, oh so tasty
So many stories but let's not be hasty
His six beady eyes scanning his surroundings

Or he might chomp the phrases
Of David Walliams' humour crazes
So, so funny
Makes him burp, burrrp!

Oh no, the beast has forgotten
The most not rotten, the dessert!
It could be a meal of mayhem
With Derek Landy!

Or it could be a nibble of ancient horror
With Joseph Delaney and a pinch of terror

The mystical tales with unbeatable language
and imagery to die for!
Alas, there is no more!

**Alishba Rameez (10)**
Loxford School, Ilford

# Haunted Diamond Queen

Do you ever think of being a queen?
Well, why can't you come along and explore this world?

*Sparkle noises*
Is the queen over there or here?
These walls and halls are really giant
I don't know where to go!

"Hello!" said the creepy queen
"Do you know the password?" asked the diamond queen
"No!" shouted the silly servant
And those crazy people lived crazily ever after

"I am the queen," said Haunted Diamond Queen
The queen is the best at scaring people
She is scary but pretty
The queen has six arms and three eyeballs
Her smile is as scary as a horror film
Her earrings are super duper shiny.

**Sibel Hassan (7)**
Loxford School, Ilford

# The Hydra

The swampy trees swish and sway
In the whistling wind every day
Some of the waters hold a mystery
It is rare you would ever get a chance to see
An undefeatable hydra.

As scary as a monster
As tough as a stone
He hides in the slimy rivers
The fiend is ever to moan.

*Splish! Splosh!*

"How dare you take a step into my lair
You challenge me to a fight? That sounds fair!"
He rises up, grumbling to the ground
Making a horrendous and horrible sound.

The horrific heads expel from their lungs
Fiery fragments, trickling off its tongues
The teeth are knives
That could tear your skin
Will you beat this undefeatable Hydra?

The putrid smell of choking breath
Will it conclude or sentence you to death?
It was time to fight
In the gloomy night
With the horrible Hydra.

His burning, deafening ruby-red eyes
Pierce through your innocent soul
Time to demolish this realm
Now it was time to overwhelm
This undefeatable Hydra.

Shaking, small thoughts filled with fear
He was standing ready, getting near and near
Can't we work together as a team?
*Ding! Ding! Ding!*
Turns out it was just a dream
Or was it?

## Ioana Daniela Craciun (9)

Loxford School, Ilford

# Beware Of Bony, The Skeleton Skull Monster

Beware of the Skeleton Skull Monster
The one who roams through town
His teeth are crooked but piercing
And coming to crush you down!
He has shaggy ears and is half hairless
With slices across his face
If you don't want to be his human feast
You have to beat his race!
His figure looks like it was sent from Hell
His eyes crimson red
When you want to go to sleep
*Gulp!* This creature won't swallow you dead.
The young men say they want to slay this creature
The fiend with bad breath and fearsome features
But they knew it was a lively dream
Even the whole world was not the biggest team.
A colossal silhouette shadowed through the gloom
There were teeth grinding slightly together
Each mouth with a story of doom.

"People of this town!
I have come to stand my ground!
I wasn't being rude
It's just my terrible mood!"
Now they knew the rattling monster's story
It was no longer gory
"Our lives will not come to an end
Come and rejoice with our brand new friend!"
*Rattle! Rattle! Shake! Shake!*
His bones clinked together
All the children pranced around him
This tale could go on forever.

## Glory'nn Helen Lartey (9)
Loxford School, Ilford

# You Have To Go To School, Trosiy

Wake up, wake up
Or unsleepable Trosiy will come
Make your bed
Make your bed
Or unsleepable, neat Trosiy will come
Brush your teeth, brush your teeth
Or unsleepable, neat, surprising, gorgeous Trosiy
will come
Brush your hair, brush your hair,
Or unsleepable, neat, surprising, gorgeous Trosiy
will come
Put your clothes on, put your clothes on
Or unsleepable, neat, surprising, gorgeous Trosiy
will come
Eat your food, eat your food,
Or unsleepable, neat, surprising, gorgeous Trosiy
will come
Put your shoes on, put your shoes on
Or unsleepable, neat, surprising, gorgeous, cute-
haired,

smart-clothed Trosiy will come
Put your bag on, put your bag on,
Or unsleepable, neat, surprising, gorgeous, cute-
haired,
smart-clothed muddy-shoed, packed Trosiy
will come
Yes, Trosiy will not come because you're done.

## Ayaat S Khan (7)
Loxford School, Ilford

# Deadly Darkness

I stayed in my bed sinking into my dreams
I dreamt of something strange
The moonlight casting eerie shadows
My smile faded away
Something snuck out of the dark
It was huge with spiky thorns
It was enveloped in wounds and scaly wings
And teeth as hard as an elephant's tusks
*Thump!*
I jumped out of my slumber
Hearing nothing except the gushing of rain
And the airy singing of the trees
I could only make out a blurred image
I was as tired as can be
But your eyes are not to deceive
A humungous figure popped out from the door
I hid under my cover
My heart missed a beat
The petrifying thing with a heart hard as a rock
And a tail tough as a wall
With claws long and sharp as a knife

And a smile which brings no good
That was a dreadful night
With the monster alright.

## Hadjer Sarah Marmouze (10)

Loxford School, Ilford

# Gobble, Gobble Green Beak!

*Creak! Squeak!*
The beaked monster murmured
I was petrified
Though the beast was barely heard
He cast a haunting shadow
Upon the darkened walls
His beak was long and narrow
He wasn't a herbivore
He glared with glowing eyes
He smelt like rotten eggs
I needed to run and hide
Before I dropped dead
I grabbed hold of my flashlight
And tiptoed down the stairs
But when I saw the 'fright'
I was laughing in tears!

His evil glowing eyes
Were cute, not like before

The smell of rotten eggs
Was breath and nothing more
When I bowed and checked
It was feisty, that's for sure
For when I reached and picked it up
He jumped right on the floor
Gobble Green Beak
Was such a clever guy
But holy guacamole
This tiny chick could fly!

## Dunstan Sodengbe (10)
Loxford School, Ilford

# The Life Of Horrific Hooligan

*Beware! Beware!*
Horrific Hooligan is a petrifying and cold-hearted creature
Trust me this beast isn't kind or mature
His personality is as cold as ice
As he'll kill any lonely mice.

*Bang! Whoosh!*
He has demolished the planet of Earth
And then he had set forth
To a dimension of woeful warriors
The king fortunately defeated the so-called 'saviours'.

Horrific Hooligan, a petrifying and cold-hearted hybrid
"Oh why, oh why does he have to live?"
If you've never seen him before and you say
"Hooligan is just a spoilt big baby!"

He will eat your body parts daily
This horrendous hybrid has a flaming fire crown
At a thousand degrees, it could probably burn a
vast village down!

**Inayah Hoque (9)**
Loxford School, Ilford

# The Doom Of A Monster

As the gloomy mist
Invades the night sky
The luminous ball
Invades the misty sky
*Awoo! Awoo!*
Mighty wolves howl
In the distance
The wind howls
And the timid leaves shiver
You are tucked in your cosy bed
Your mum says, "Night-night
Sleep tight, hope the bed bugs don't bite."
Inch by inch
Your closet opens
Creepy dolls rain off the ceiling
Millions of spiders try to suffocate you!
In fear you try to run
You turn around
What do you see?
A colossal monster!
With razor-sharp teeth

He takes colossal steps
Closer and closer to you
He takes one more step
You expect him to eat you
But instead he plays with you
Ha! That gave you a shock
Although
Be aware of monsters.

## Vinushika Chandragumar (10)
Loxford School, Ilford

# Evil Hideous Glow Comes To Town

*Stomp, stomp, stomp*
The monster came with a big thump
His name was Hideous Glow
People called him Evil Glow
"Why did Glow come to town?"

He always wakes up at night
And is ready to fight
He is a terrifying monster in the world
"Why did Glow come to town?"

He is a nasty mechanical monster
Who does not like chemicals
People all hide under their beds
"Why did Glow come to town?"

I hope you don't see him
Because his claws are right under your bed
Peeking out
Can't he go somewhere else
"Why did Glow come to town?"

*Boom!*
He starts to fight
Then he hears a baby start to cry
"Why did Glow come to town?"

## Bhavya M Patel (9)
Loxford School, Ilford

# Rainbow Is Who I Am!

You are one of a kind
A bunny which is beyond divine
So many different shades within you
Where do I start?
I haven't got a clue.

Let me start with the pure richness within you
Your cheeks go rosy red
Whenever a compliment is said
Your face glows as bright as the sun
Whenever your friends are near
You're pale pink when your smile beams across the
room
Just like the moon.

Your heart is blue whenever you're sad
Your heart burns like fire
Whenever you huff and puff heavily
You're pale and sweaty when you feel unsteady
Even if you look like a monster
You will be a rainbow

Even if you have yellow fur
Even if you have a silver heart
You are a rainbow within.

## Nailah Ansari (10)
Loxford School, Ilford

# The Dark Demon!

Once there lived a dark, isolated demon
He was very frightening and hairy
This monstrous, mischievous creature can kill you
Trust me, he is very scary.

He has red, bloody horns
This barbaric brute only comes out in the gloomy
night
This shape-shifter is spotty and has sharp, pointy
jaws
He is a vile, dangerous fright.

This atrocious, pathetic swine
Could gobble you up in a bite
The detestable savage
Is the opposite of a bright light.

This horrendous, horrible fiend
Loves to eat
He could eat anything he desires
He has smelly, horrifying feet.

This terrible, gnarly beast
Has to go to bed
Beware!
Tomorrow you might be dead.

**Zaynah Malik (9)**
Loxford School, Ilford

# Halloween Slammer!

*Silence. Fear. Anger. Smash. Crash!*

People tremble and dodge
The monster's green slimy slodge
As the moon starts to rise
Slammer starts to terrorise!

Slammer is the monster
Who represents Halloween
He has horns as sharp as knives
That will make you want to scream!

Sneaky, slimy, Slammer
Arose from a pumpkin patch
As he stomped across the field
Squashing all the pumpkins flat.

As the sun starts to appear
The beast starts to fade
People start to cry
About all the mess he'd made.

Will this beast return?
Nobody knows for sure

Everybody starts to wonder
If he will come back for more!

**Harrison Li (9)**
Loxford School, Ilford

# The Suspicious Monster

I could feel a strong eerie presence of spirits
I could hear a person singing lyrics
I could feel the wind starting to whip heavily
I could taste a peppermint sweet from the cold breeze.

I started to shiver
I could feel a figure
I looked back to see a sack
I wanted to hide
But I could only see an abandoned house in the mist
It was a big risk.

I could see a bulky, scaly, green monster
I could smell seaweed, yuck
I could hear noises coming closer and nearer
I could feel his frustration growing stronger and bigger.

I told the monster a nice compliment
The monster whispered twice
That I brightened his day.

**Asmaa Sakkaf (10)**
Loxford School, Ilford

90

# My Big Ray

Big Ray
Awake at night and asleep during the day
His skin is very slimy and he smells rather bad
Smartly dressed with a bow tie
No hair and one big eye
He makes everyone laugh
But he seriously needs a bath
His teeth are all wonky
When he speaks, he sounds like a donkey
He has massive feet which flip and flop
All around the street
He has a cheeky little grin
And a cute little dimple in his chin
He has four fingers and three toes
One small eye and one big nose
He wiggles like a snake
And dances like moving water in a lake
But I don't care what anyone thinks of Big Ray
He's my favourite monster in every way.

**Ayaan Nasir (7)**
Loxford School, Ilford

# Fiery Fight!

At night there was a doom on the door
Suddenly, when I opened the door
I saw a fire monster fighting an ice monster
The monster was so cool, he could buy a pool
I hid in my secret basement
I brought all my friends and cousins into my room
I saw a fiery, furry planet and it felt like doom
I was sending the monster fight to YouTube
The ice monster was a cruel villain
It was more than a year
It was lasting for two years
Which I couldn't bear
I loved the epic battle
It was amazing and astonishing
I put 2,000 pounds on the monster winning
The ice monster was injured
It was like an action movie
The ice monster lost.

## Rushaanth Jeyakumar (7)
Loxford School, Ilford

# Beast Girl, The One And Only

Beast Girl, Beast Girl,
Likes to twirl.
It makes her feel like a girl.
She has three eyes but not a nose,
She does, however, have very hairy toes.
Her nails are long, that's for sure,
She gets a weekly manicure.

She gallops through the woods like a gazelle,
She knows the way very well.
One day in the forest came little Maurice,
He had with him, his big brother Borice.

You better watch your way,
When you go out to play.
Be alert and don't get hurt
Or you will be her dessert!
Make sure you hide from this monster,
She is the world's greatest chompster!

## Ayesha Malik (9)
Loxford School, Ilford

# The Creature

The creature was born in a volcano
During the day he rested in the scorching lava
When the sun set, he rose tall and high
His eyes as red as fire
Stood out against the black night sky
His body was made of ashy rocks
With molten lava pouring out the cracks
He stomped through the blackened trees
Heading to the city
He walked through the silent streets
I saw him through the window
I was rooted to the spot by fear
I waited for him to pass by
Before I took another breath
I went to my bed and hid under the covers
And from that night on
I didn't look out the window again.

**Azim Ahmed Ali (10)**
Loxford School, Ilford

# Slug Bug

There was once a monster known as Slug Bug.
He liked nothing more than to hug hug.
He had four eyes and a long green body.
All he wanted to do was love somebody.

All the children called him scary,
And told him that he was big and hairy.
He was as tall as a tree and as big as a house.
But when he spoke, he was as quiet as a mouse.

There was a wee boy, who was called Roy.
He was nice and kind and shared his toy.
They played and played and rode their bikes,
Until it was very late at night.
They went round and round along the bend,
Until they became the very best friends.

**Zahra Malik (7)**
Loxford School, Ilford

# Bedtime Nightmare

Whilst sleeping in my duvet
I heard growls as loud as a pride of lions
I shivered with fear
And my mind asked itself
What is it? Where is it?
Then I opened my eyes
Silent eyes stared at me with curiosity
I saw it pounce on me, but it missed
I scrambled out of bed with terror.
I ran to the bedroom door as fast as a speeding
Mercedes
But before I touched the knob
I realised the monster didn't want to eat me
She wanted to have a playmate
So I played until midnight
I'll never forget her snuggling with me
Do you want a monster? Remember, it is not for
free.

**David Fowowe (10)**
Loxford School, Ilford

# The Green Goblin

My monster is as frightening as a ghost
She only goes to the east coast
She isn't the angel you think
When you look at her, you can't even blink
You'll turn to stone and forever be alone.

She smells really sweet
And thinks humans are the perfect treat
She wears a torn-up hoodie
Where she stores all her goodies.

Green Goblin has a life
She kills anyone with a knife
She has emerald green skin
And loves to win.

The emerald creature
Says being a goblin is in her true nature
She's not kind
So don't play with her mind!

**Simrah Ahmed (7)**
Loxford School, Ilford

# Super Symbiote

Living on the edge
Fighting crime, spinning webs
Swinging from the highest ledges
He can leap above our heads.

Villains on the rise
And the cities victimised
Looking up with no surprise
Arriving in the speed of time.

Super Super Symbiote
Super Super Symbiote.

Crawling through the night
Facing evil with his might
He's a hero in our eyes
See the headlights every time.

Making villains fall
Webbing rivals to a halt
Racing up and down
The walls bringing justice to us all!

Super Super Symbiote
Super Super Symbiote.

## Muhammad Abdullah Cheema (10)
Loxford School, Ilford

# Midnight The Monster

This monster comes from a cave
With bats and scurrying rats
At the deepest, darkest midnight
He comes out to give you a fright.

He has horns on his rock-like head
And his eyes are blazing red
He has a long spiky tail
With thorns as sharp as nails.

His name is Midnight as he doesn't like the light
When he gets angry, he wants to start a fight
*Crash! Thump! Kaboom!*
As he destroys another room.

Midnight is a monster
Don't ever get in his way
Because if you do, oh dear, poor you
You'll find you'll have to pay.

**Gwyneth Li (7)**
Loxford School, Ilford

# Haunted Hollow House

*Ding dong!*
As I entered the haunted house
There was a growl
It was my stomach
I saw some leftover turkey
Before I could take a bite of turkey
I heard a noise
It was the creature.

He howls at night
When the moon shines bright
He is as loud as a crowd
You better watch out
Because he is as sneaky as an agent
He knows what will happen
Because he has nine eyes
He can pick up twelve humans at once
Because he was twelve arms and twelve hands
He is strong
He runs as fast as a cheetah
Because he has ten legs and ten feet.

**Nidhirav Surendar (7)**
Loxford School, Ilford

# Vemon The Demon

Vemon was a demon
A demon who never ate a lemon
Big, bad and strong
His ferocious claws could crack metal.

Vemon was a demon
His eyes were red peppers
Crackling in a rampant fire
His body filled with a roller coaster of anger
Vemon's armoured body
Unattainable to defeat.

Vemon was a demon
Invincible, savage and a threatening monster
Hard to defeat
Easy to fail.

Vemon was a demon
Spiky claws the size of knives
Eyes as big as dinner plates
A lightning bolt to shock monsters.

Beware, he might get you!

## Vihaan Parvatini (9)
Loxford School, Ilford

# The Angry Beast

All monsters aren't scary
But they're all hairy
My monster is very scary and very hairy
He snores at night
But I don't get a fright
He plays monster games in his deep, dark cave
He has big teeth to eat you all up like a caterpillar.

He stares out of the window in the cold night
But when I look at him
He gets a big fright
Make sure he doesn't see you
Or you'll be trapped between his jaws
He likes eating children
To him it is a perfect treat
I can feel the red eyes watching me
While every other child is falling asleep.

**Alayna Malik (8)**
Loxford School, Ilford

# Rosie The Monster!

Rosie is a very cute and adorable monster
She likes to laugh until the sun rises
She likes to be helpful
But whenever she growls loudly be aware
She might get really angry
You will get gobbled up in her really little tummy
The gorgeous monster sings a really kind-hearted lullaby
Until every single child is snoring.

Rosie is a very cute and adorable monster
She smells like butter
She sounds like buzzing bees
When she dances around
Her sharp ears twinkle
Like beautiful bright shooting stars
Rosie brings happiness to her friends and family.

**Tiana Satheeskaran (9)**
Loxford School, Ilford

# Smooth Slick

I can hear you Smooth Slick
Under my bed planning a music trick
Boombox, disco, moves and sounds
Oh my god, your lyrics are profound.

I can see you Smooth Slick
On the edge of my bed is your shape-shifting
shadow
Check out those slimy moves
Wow, is that Captain Jack Sparrow?

I can feel you Smooth Slick
Climbing the wall to get this party started
Your fur and warmth makes me sleepy
Oh my days, you are so creepy.
*Roarrr!*

My eyes are open
And the door is broken
Was this a dream
Or was it real?

**Jalal Khan (9)**
Loxford School, Ilford

# Felipe's Revenge

Once upon a time he was hungry
Once upon a time he felt joy
Once upon a time he was happy
Once upon a time he was a decoy.

Felipe had had enough
Of all the abuse he'd been through
He was just a mannequin head
But he still wanted to learn the truth.

He was soon thrown and destroyed
He was really sad
But an evil force brought him back to life
And allowed him to continue his plan.

So be careful at night, kids
Felipe wants to get his revenge
He is looking for his master
He will get his revenge.

**Ali Keita Mbalo (11)**
Loxford School, Ilford

# About Slickach

Slickach smells like sewers where there are bugs
He never stops munching and eating
His slimy, sticky jelly is all around.

He loves making sounds that bother people
*Boom! Bang! Crash!* There goes another house
The city hates Slickach
Slickach loves baking.

He loves eating bricks, soaked bloody bodies
He hates proper food that's very nice
One last thing is that he is so heavy.

At night he glows with his big spots on him
People can see and hear him on roads
He hates it just like kids hate broccoli.

**Tanjil Islam (9)**
Loxford School, Ilford

# All About Bones

Bones is the evilest monster of them all
He takes over the world and is very tall
He makes everyone cry and lives in a hall
The first place he started doing evil was at the
mall.

Bones took over the mall by doing this
He asked a girl out and got rejected
He got super mad and started a mess
He just wanted to date and didn't mean the rest.

He realised what he had done and said sorry
Then they were all happy and lived long
They crossed the street and saw a lorry
And heard the bell which went *ding-dong!*

## Muhammad Eshan Kamran (9)
Loxford School, Ilford

# Slimy Sid

I can feel you Slimy Sid
Your plump, wobbly belly
Feels like strawberry-flavoured jelly!

I can hear you Slimy Sid
Whilst your yellow teeth are chattering
You make slime that is flattering!

I can see you Slimy Sid
Your one glowing, glistening eye
Shines so bright like a star in the sky!

I can smell you Slimy Sid
Your revolting breath floats through the air
It smells like burnt egg cooked by a bear!

I really like you Slimy Sid
Your rubbery orange arm
Tickles me, making me alarmed!

## Zahra Khan (10)
Loxford School, Ilford

# Monster's Wishes

Oobajuba wishes for this and that and this
Oops, he shouldn't have wished for that!
Where are my wishes? Oh, splendid!
Here comes Cloesours
A girl he's been seeing to change
*Boosh, troosh! Boosh, troosh! Boosh, troosh!*
I have a secret
A magic power you won't believe
It's like a superpower
Ooba is always complaining
About being clean on the outside
When it's the inside that counts
What was his wish?
It was to have a good appearance
And be good on the inside and outside combined!

**Evelyn Bexigas Soares (8)**
Loxford School, Ilford

# The Terrifying Soul Stealer

Beware of the Soul Stealer
For that is his name
Do not come near him
Because he will make you go insane
Don't challenge the Soul Stealer
Because he's the best in the game
Be petrified of the Soul Stealer
And say your prayers before you sleep
Because he might be under your bed!
He will get in your head
If you see him
You will shake and wish for it to be the end of him
Which is for-never!
You will regret the day you have ever met
Or messed with the terrific, terrible
Mind-hunting Soul Stealer.

**Aliza Jumah Ali (8)**
Loxford School, Ilford

# My Monster Is...

My monster is creepy
My monster is eerie
My monster is huge
So you might want to move
My monster is pointy
So pointy she can cut you in the blink of an eye
My monster is Sharpy!

My monster is on your wall
My monster is on your ceiling
So please be reading
My monster is in your wooden cupboard
Spying on Mother Hubbard
My monster is in your smelly kitchen
Because she doesn't want to listen
My monster is under your bouncy bed
So please be careful when you go there
My monster is Sharpy!

**Raynah Shukri (7)**
Loxford School, Ilford

# The Critter Under The Stairs

The hideous critter under the stairs
Is not scary but she is hairy
She is not a boy or a toy
She has eight eyes
And she is always staying up late till midnight.

She is as green as a fresh cucumber
She is a Minotaur
She doesn't go to school because she is a fool.

When she hears the stomp of the humans
The critter eats parents but not children
The monster is as naughty as a baby
She lays ten eggs at a time.

I found out her name
It is Crazy Daisy
And she is funny, smart and happy.

**Iman Majid (7)**
Loxford School, Ilford

# Halloween Screams

Halloween Screams
Yeah, that's me
I'm big and mean
I'm all you see
Orange and green
Grrr!

Halloween Screams
I'm in your dreams
Big and mean
Great, sharp teeth
I'm underneath
Grrr, your bed, grrr!

Halloween Screams
You came for me
I'm not free
So scary
Just not for me
Hee hee!

Halloween screams
I regret having these haunting dreams

I wish I had my own house
Now I screech as loud as a mouse
Screech, screech!

**Mahnoor Nisa Malik (9)**
Loxford School, Ilford

# Wild-Eyed Green Monsters

I can hear the monster in the field with a ferocious growl,
I can hear them laugh and I can hear them talk,
I can hear they have reached the door,
I can hear the door opening as they reach my bedroom door,
As they open the door...

Wide-eyed green monsters at my door,
Trembling hands open it,
Jumping, skipping
They come in,
Let's all party!
Yeah!
Party time, having fun,
We're in a line dancing to songs,
Sticking out our tongues,
Our lungs popping out,
We all fall over one by one.

**Alisha Majeed**
Loxford School, Ilford

# The Whisper Monster

Do you hear the hard spiky skin monster
The Whisper Monster is near
Then turn away your scary ear
Don't you see its red, long fangs facing you
They'll stop and look at you
Don't you ignore the smoky, rough hair
Don't you dare!
The girl who died he tried to save
She'll die again inside the giant's grave
This monster must fall, as they must
The fate of all is always dust
His friends are lost
Unless he goes to Trenzalore
The trap is set for his friends
They travel when he ends!

**Sumaiya Khan (9)**
Loxford School, Ilford

# Demi Deadly!

Demi Deadly is a bloodthirsty beast
Go a step near him
You'll end up as a feast
His razor-sharp teeth, sharper than knives
Your mouth-watering flesh is what he thrives on.

Why oh why does it have to be me?
All I want is to be free
My life is at the brink of death
Oh, please don't let this be my final breath!

Intelligent Idelli, the heroic lord
Will slash this brutal fiend with a slice of his sword
This menacing monster is far off dead
*Slash!* All is left is his blood ruby-red.

**Shanti Panesar (9)**
Loxford School, Ilford

# Monster In My House!

Stop... Still... Silent
Scream!
Icky slime dropping down her back
Making the creaky stairs crack
Tangly, twisty, horrid hair
But she doesn't even care.

Now just look at this poor old child
He must think that he is wild
Listen to that rude grunting sound
Will Grinda ever be found?

Just stare at her deadly eyes
There awaits a stunning surprise
For sure you will get hypnotised
Just remind yourself, her eyes...
Stop... Still... Silent
Scream!
Beware of Grinda!

**Kshaf Naqvi (9)**
Loxford School, Ilford

# The Hungry Monster

The monster went to the park
The children didn't run away
From the big, giant monster
The monster said,
"Don't run away, I won't eat you!"
So the children went with him
And they were friends forever
They went home, playing together
And they were eating a lot of pizza
The big bad monster was laughing
The children said,
"What's the matter with you?"
He said, "I am going to eat you!"
The children were screaming
Then the monster ate them all.

## Isabel Garrouch Girón (8)
Loxford School, Ilford

# The Gobble Monster

The Gobble Monster would love a good munch
But he never gets a great lunch
The poor monster would always give a punch
To his empty, sorrowful belly.

*Rumble!*
The monster was as skinny as a stick
And couldn't stop feeling sick
He'd been sitting next to a dusty brick
Begging for tasty food.

He always cried and cried
Thinking about chicken that is fried
People will always hide
From the hungry creature.

The Gobble Monster
Will starve and starve.

**Iyaz Korim (9)**
Loxford School, Ilford

# The Monster

I thought I saw a monster
Underneath my bed
His eyes were yellow
And his hair was red... *grr!*

I thought I saw a monster
Underneath my chair
His face was green
And he looked really mean - *sss!*

I thought I saw a monster
In my bedroom last night
His ears were pink
And his teeth ware shape-shifting crocodiles -
*gighzshhhdit!*

I thought I saw a monster
And that he saw me
But don't tell anyone
Or they will be mad at me.

## Daniya Ahmed (8)
Loxford School, Ilford

# The Secret Of Hookfang!

Down in a deep dark cave
Lived a small but terrifying monster
They called him... Hookfang!
People in the village also called him
The scary shape-shifter
He strolled into the village at night
And gave little children the fright
No one dared to talk about him
For he would haunt them
Till their very last breath
The villages uncovered his deadly secret
And found out...
He was afraid of dogs!
So from then on
They kept hundreds of dogs in their village!

## Sharleez Ghouri (9)
Loxford School, Ilford

# The Hukean

Have you ever wondered about the Hukean?
It has eyes
As thin as rice
It has a hat
That looks like a bat
It has nails
And it isn't from Wales
It has horns
Which is how it was born.

It has a tattoo
That is a racoon
It isn't always happy
But its cousin's name is Flappy
It frightens people to death
Because that's what it can do best
The Hukean can be coming to you now!
So when he approaches, don't forget to bow.

**Syon Danny Maisuria (10)**
Loxford School, Ilford

# Chaos Ghoul

It's a monster
It's a monster
It's... Chaos Ghoul!
He is as yellow as a lemon
He is seven

He is buff
He is tough
You may think he's ugly
But he's fuzzy
Chaos Ghoul is not funny

Chaos Ghoul is mean
He is unclean, ew!
Why does he like to eat dogs
But adores cats?
He has a job to eat humans
But doesn't like it
He is nice
Because he doesn't eat us
After all, let's not make a fuss.

**Sana Chithara (9)**
Loxford School, Ilford

# There's A Monster Under My Bed!

There's a monster under my bed
Once I saw his green, slimy head
Once I heard his malicious roar
Once I heard him scraping with his claw.

There's a monster under my bed
His eyes are evil, glowing red
He always looks for children to feast
He is such a terrible beast.

There's a monster under my bed
What if this monster wants me dead
I always smell rotten meat
Which this monster loves to eat.

Will this monster eat me?

**Saarah Badawood (9)**
Loxford School, Ilford

# The Spiky Monster

The spiky monster walks through the woods
Listening to children's sounds
If the monster catches a glimpse of you
You'll be hung by the big grave grounds.

He growls like a roaring lion
In the middle of an eerie night
He likes creating some violence
By coming for a deadly monster fight.

So one thing you should do
Is to lock yourself in the room
So that when we see the morning sun
We know that doomsday for monsters has begun.

**Rahman Syed (10)**
Loxford School, Ilford

# The Vicious Beast

The wretched beast smelt like static electricity
The scent of electricity was here automatically
Its tremendous tail was as large as an elephant
Does anyone know if it's relevant?

As the monster walked through the dark night
His tail swinging from side to side
Shining so bright
He stopped and stared to see
If there were any lights.

Oh my god
I thought he had seen me
In his head he was thinking
He was going to get a bite!

**Nia Edo-Sarfo (10)**
Loxford School, Ilford

# Something Is Waiting...

Something is in the darkness
It's shuffling near the door
Although I can't be sure
It followed me home
And took a stone
It's under my bed
Now for sure.

I see a peeping head
Its eyes are deep, dark red
I wish I could turn on the light
But then it would have been too bright
The smell of rotten flesh reached my nose
Just then, something tickled my toes
Is this a dream?
Did I spot a tree...
Or a monster?

**Ariana Gandacov (9)**
Loxford School, Ilford

# I Thought I Saw A Monster Under My Bed

I thought I saw a monster
It had yellow eyes
Its mouth was as big as an ostrich egg
Its teeth were sharp as knives
He smelled like rotten cheese
He was as green as leaves
He was as huge as two children
When I looked under my bed, there was nothing
But when I looked behind me
I saw the monster
Then it gobbled me up
I realised it was a dream
Then I saw green footprints
I saw my dog
All this time, the dog was the monster!

**Tasin Rashadul Huq (7)**
Loxford School, Ilford

# Deadly Beasts

On a quest
To do the best
And sneakily in the night
The monster's on a quest for a fight
To haunt another beastly beast
And have humans to feast!
He is half-robot, half-dragon
But a little clumsy
However he has sharp shark teeth
And spits green, poisonous, lethal acid.
He lives in a deep, dark, deadly abandoned mine
And he harvests human flesh
And this is horrifying, not fine!
In the night
He'll put up a fight.

## Manveer Lota (10)
Loxford School, Ilford

# Crusty: Friend Or Foe?

At the dead of midnight
I could hear
Something stomping loudly
With my ear.

Something huge,
Something scary,
Something tall,
Something hairy.

His eyes were as bright as fire,
Horns as pointy as teeth.
His skin as rough as sandpaper,
His body as tall as trees.

But if you got to know him,
You would surprisingly find.
He is kind,
He is cheeky,
He is helpful,
He is my friend, Crusty!

**Aaminah Moosa (10)**
Loxford School, Ilford

132

# The Afterlife Monster

When you die
You will go to Heaven if you're good
But if you are very bad
You will go to Hell
So if you're bad
You have to face me
Because I always win
So you must eat a bin.

I am as red as a Ferrari
When you're here you will burn more
But then you get to explore
If you want to sleep
There will be no beds
Because many people are dead
And if you sleep on a bed
It will explode.

**Mustafa Ashraf (8)**
Loxford School, Ilford

# Miss Monster

Miss Monster is an eerie problem
She goes crunch, crunch, crunch
And munch, munch, munch
She is a shape-shifter
What about the lake lifter
She lurks around at night waiting to fight
You can see her anywhere
If there is time to spare
There is slime oozing out of her ears
It always appears
She can lift zebras
Her friend's name is Debra
She snores loudly
Better not roar
Miss Monster is the lobster!

**Maryam Ali (8)**
Loxford School, Ilford

# Beware Of Monsters!

*Crash! Boom! Kaboom!*
The Joker likes to clown around
Like he's in a circus
He could feel the smell of smoke
Coming from the clouds
I could taste the sour anger of the Joker
The people are in danger of this terrifying monster.

"What should we do?"
"The people hope he will die!"
"Stop, stop, stop!"
"As he came to end the world!"
"Should we run?"

## Faheem Ismail (9)
Loxford School, Ilford

# Amy And The Slug

Once upon a time there was a beautiful monster
Her name was Amy
She was very kind and funny
She had four legs and three hands on each side
She had pretty hair and lovely teeth
She loved flowers
She wished she had a picnic
Then she saw a beautiful slug
They both said hello, hello
They went out to different shops
But the slug, he was still shy
He would never talk
He would just say hello, hello.

**Zaina Munir (7)**
Loxford School, Ilford

# The Monster Of Doom

My monster ate children
He went hunting for children
So he went looking in the forest
He found a child and ate him up
Then he wanted to look for meat to eat
So he went looking for lamb
He found some lamb to eat
Then he went looking for the flying potion
And then he was flying.

He was looking for octopuses
He went to the seaside
To look for some octopuses
Then he went into the sea.

## Zain Khan (8)
Loxford School, Ilford

# Beware Of Beastly Bob

He stomps about in the eerie night
He will give you a terrible fright
He has a giant hairy back
Beware of his sack!

His body might be filled with cotton
However his teeth are definitely rotten
Just make sure you stay alert
Because you can get really hurt.

His red glazing eyes of fire
Tell you that he is a liar
The beast has a deep voice
But what can he do? He has no choice.

**Kisaa Naqvi (10)**
Loxford School, Ilford

# Sneaky Mysterio

The sneaky, sly, ferocious monster
Creeps onto you aggressively
When the sky is pitch-black
His vast eyes watch you every time
Waiting to strike
He is a vicious beast
Looking for his prey
He is like a lion
That hasn't eaten for months
His muscles are as big as you
He shows no mercy when he finds you
He hides behind every lurking corner of your room
So he might come to you.

**Rayyan Rahman (8)**
Loxford School, Ilford

# The Monstrous Misconception

Many people do believe
That monsters' hearts are full of greed
But there is one monster I know
She is very nice, let me show
She is as pretty as a flower
And also has a kind of power
She also is enormously helpful
Towards little children she is zestful
If you meet her, she meets you warmly
Not the monsters who meet dimly
Let's make the monsters happy
Not so horribly nasty!

**Kinza Naveed (9)**
Loxford School, Ilford

# The Child Eater

Behind the trees
Adjacent to the seas
Lives a ferocious beast
Who has kids for his feast
With teeth as sharp as swords.

Beware young people
He hides near the steeple
He sneaks up to you, discreet
And finds you to eat
He licks his lips.

His teeth are gleaming
His eyes are shining
Causing a huge plight
With pure delight
To eat you as fast as light.

**Rashvin Udawatte (10)**
Loxford School, Ilford

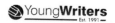

# Monster Madness

I just heard a sound
It came from the ground
Here he is again
The hairy scary 'Gogalops'
Please, make it stop.

Buzzing away like a flickering light
His horns and breath give me a fright
When he is asleep he loudly snores
If you're not careful
You'll be trapped in his jaws.

He loudly stomps across the street
He thinks eating humans is his treat.

## Aman Singh Bedi (9)
Loxford School, Ilford

# The Gooey, Germy Fiend

Here comes the terrifying Gloogy
The one who is gooey
Don't make a noise or he will come
Coming for a feast with a nom!

The shape-shifter crawling on the floor
With slime and a lot more
A nightmare that is horror as we know
This is just a big no!

The monster who is a germy fiend
Is not a fluffy friend
Now as evil as the evil beast
No feasting with him!

**Safwan Khan (9)**
Loxford School, Ilford

# Gexaploop

*Stomp, stomp, stomp!*
Here he comes
His stomach's as hungry as a tyrannosaurus rex
Hide your burgers
They are the best
*Munch, munch, munch!*
Someone's coming...
It's Gexaploop!
His jaws are as large as your TV
His teeth are as sharp as a knife
That could take away your life
And all he eats is your burgers
But for now it's nap time.

## Sheikh Monim (8)
Loxford School, Ilford

# The Monster

Help!
There is a monster in the hall
He is tall
The monster is as white as a ghost
And he loves a piece of toast.

Argh!
One day I'm going to trap him
The net will jump on him
I'll stare at his horrible face
His breath is the worst taste.

While we are asleep
We may become his treat
But I'll fight
And I can fight like a knight.

**Haleema Faisal (9)**
Loxford School, Ilford

# Candy The Sleep Monster

She snoops through houses at night
Giving frights to those
Who are awake during midnight
To those who are good, they get lovely dreams
Those who are bad, get ready
Frights are coming your way.
Under the bed, growling and howling
The smoke of red coming from under the bed
Roams through every house that makes a single peep
Off she goes - *bang, crash, thump!*

## Eshal Hassan (8)
Loxford School, Ilford

# Andromeda, Andromeda

Andromeda, Andromeda
Above all
A demonic gaze, once bright, now hellfire
Nothing to admire.

*Bang! Whoosh!*

Andromeda, Andromeda
Haunting the woods, day and night
Don't bring up a fight
He will execute you with all of his might.

I get judged for my appearance
I get judged for my power.

Was this what I was meant to be?

**Adan Uddin (10)**
Loxford School, Ilford

# Soul Taker

He creeps up on you in the dark
Behind your garden's tree bark
He comes past your toy car park
Then he calls his hawk
He kidnaps you and eats you for a feast!

Beware, he is lurking
His tummy likes to make a gurgle
He likes the colour purple
So he gobbles you up!

You should leave a snack
Because in his sack
He has a pack
Of creatures.

**Nethwan Udawatte (8)**
Loxford School, Ilford

# The Monster That Always Comes For Halloween

I sometimes wonder who it could be
That there's a monster living inside of me?
Only one monster tends to be here
Passing through years and years
It comes out with a fright
He always comes for Halloween
He's as evil as a vampire
He wants nothing but a treat
As darkness falls beneath the shadows
Outside your house
This monster is called
Ranger-Mo.

**Zahra Esmaeili (8)**
Loxford School, Ilford

# Mischievous Monster

My monster does not have a car
But he came from very far
He jumped out of a roller coaster
So we call him Mischievous Monster.

He looks so horrible
And is never sensible
He has a gooey skin
Just like a fishy fin.

His favourite food is cheese
But he likes it with peas
Sometimes when he eats cake
He can't wait for it to bake.

**Huriyah Iqbal (8)**
Loxford School, Ilford

# Reo Loves Oreo

I know a monster called Reo,
Who loves to eat Oreo.
He's as hairy as a gorilla
And he eats pizza with mozzarella!

He roams in the heavy rain,
Without having any pain.
He sleeps all day being so lazy,
And wakes up all night like a crazy!

He roars around the city,
Having no pity.
He bangs on every door,
And shouts for more!

**Rayan Khurram (8)**
Loxford School, Ilford

# Monster Madness

Monsters are not always scary
Even though they are hairy
My monster's name is Rosie Rose
And she never steps in to pose.

She has so many horns
And she always gets stuck in thorns.

Her voice is as loud as thunder
How she feels as a monster, I wonder.

She is never full of sadness
But she goes crazy with madness.

**Bani Kaur Bedi (8)**
Loxford School, Ilford

# Monster Poem

I saw something
What was it?
It looked fluffy and it was so soft
It looked cute and small
It was little, aw
It was near a mountain
It was on a hill
What was it called?
Andrew? Sophie?
It's hard but still
Samira? Nimra? No
It does not matter
Maybe I hope the name could be...
Sweety!
Sweety the monster.

**Syeda Hamnah Shah (7)**
Loxford School, Ilford

# Dragstor, King Of All Dragons

Dragstor the dragon
Is very vile
He spits enchanted fire
So don't dare to fight.

He has great power
And lies in his keep
So don't wake the dragon
While he's asleep.

He destroys anything in his path
So get ready to feel his wrath
He devours cities one by one
So is he gonna demolish the sun?

**Ismaeel Azhar Ashraf (9)**
Loxford School, Ilford

# The Bloodsucking Beast

The bloodsucking beast
Eats humans for a feast
He sneaks into your house
As quiet as a mouse.

Trees crouch not to be seen
Everybody warns not to be mean
He influences to do something bad
It might make someone sad.

He sucks your blood
Maybe gets you stuck in mud
Under your bed
Just to make you flee.

**Iman Choudhri (9)**
Loxford School, Ilford

# There's A Monster Outside My Window!

A dark, evil, villain monster
Walks across the street
Until he gets outside your window
When you are sleeping
If you are awake
He won't be there to greet you
Instead he wants to eat you
When you are awake
Try to sleep
Or he will turn you into cake
If he spots you he will say hello
And you will turn yellow!

**Adyan Rahman (7)**
Loxford School, Ilford

# Monsters!

**M** any different creatures walk around
**O** n a night like tonight
**N** ot because it's Christmas
**S** o let's stop singing Jingle Bells
**'T** is because it's Halloween
**E** veryone beware
**R** eal monsters walk around
**S** aying 'trick or treat' everywhere.

Beware!

## Sara Arif (7)

Loxford School, Ilford

# Malicious Monsters

I can see a monster scary and red
It could run behind you and eat you in your bed
I can hear the eerie sounds coming from
downstairs
It could be eating my snacks but who cares!
I can feel the monster coming up the stairs
It has eyes and legs, all in pairs
It could even take down a tree
You better not let it free!

**Zain Butt (10)**
Loxford School, Ilford

# This Is Sleepy Simon's Life...

Hello
My name is Sleepy Simon
I am lazy as well as crazy
I can feel my three orange eyes
At the same time as me eating three scrumptious pies
Dessert
I want to go back to bed
Same as my best friend Ned
Delicious
I had a full wafer with whipped cream
Urgh
Better go back to bed
Goodnight!

## Khadija Asghar (9)
Loxford School, Ilford

# The Monster Who Said 'Goodnight'

Have you ever thought about my spiky claws
Or pointy sharp horns
I know I look extremely hairy
So people genuinely think I'm very scary.

It was that time of day I was going on my journey
Which I knew would make me very thirsty
The mountain had heaps of snow
And from the sun I could see a glow.

**Yasmin Mudhir Sharif (9)**
Loxford School, Ilford

# Wow

Zaga Waga Doodle is such a great poodle
His fluffy eyes smell like a great pie
His tall legs can go as fast as a cheetah
He is so fast
Some people may follow him
You are a shining diamond
He is impressive
But also scary
He is different
He has four eyes, wow!
I can see his skeleton.

## Hassan Jaferi (8)
Loxford School, Ilford

# The Wild Snooze

This monster loves to snooze
He's got the world record
For the biggest snooze ever
If you want his attention
I doubt you'll get it.

He is as sleepy as me
No, only joking!
As vicious as a snake when you wake him up
Do not mess with him, please
You'll regret it.

## Ibsham Ahmed (8)
Loxford School, Ilford

# Monster

Help, there's a spooky monster
Run, there's a giant spooky monster
I'm so scared
When is this hairy monster going to go?
When is this ugly, scary monster going to go?
His breath is as stinky as a sock
His nails are as sharp as a pencil
His mouth is as big as a lion's!

**Khadija Farhan Khan (7)**
Loxford School, Ilford

# Dawnsoul, Dawnsoul

Dawnsoul, Dawnsoul
He only comes out in the night
And never comes out in the light
It will give you a fright
After all, it only comes out at night
Beware!
Because it bites
He's as dark as night
So if it is bright
It won't be out
He only comes out in the night.

**Sunni White (9)**
Loxford School, Ilford

# The Hour Of Franken-Ghost

The Franken-Ghost
Comes out at night
He's really gross
So he'll give you a fright.
He's slimy and slow
Half-zombie, half-ghost
His skull is cracked
His brain shows.
The toxic terror
He'll gobble you up
With big sharp teeth
He'll never stop.

**Abdullah Khan (9)**
Loxford School, Ilford

# Everything About Mr Bubbly

**B** is for Bubbly, yes that's my name
**U** is for understanding, yes, that's what I am
**B** is for brave, yes I am strong!
**B** is for brainy, I'm a clever clogs
**L** is for love, that's what I spread
**Y** is for yearning and all I yearn for is fun!

**Yusuf Ahmed (8)**
Loxford School, Ilford

# Who's That?

As the monster entered
Dark blood started to drip, drip, drip
I heard a growling noise
That I had never heard of
And I turned around
The window was wide open
I felt warm breath on my face
That was getting warmer each second
I turned around
Nothing.

**Jannat Al-Zara Haq (10)**
Loxford School, Ilford

# The Ghost Hunter!

He will always come to you
He is invisible
So he can kill you
He catches people by running fast
Grabs them hard, eating them fast
He is the size of a white spotty cow
He is red like fire
His eyes are scary like a vampire
He has sharp teeth like a shark.

**Yusuf Aamir (7)**
Loxford School, Ilford

# Meogo The Greedy Monster

Meogo is as poisonous as a witch's potion.
Meogo is like a slimy snail.
Meogo eats cats and mats.
Meogo goes to school and jumps into the pool.
Meogo opened the door and it went bang!
Meogo eats pans and cans.
Meogo's teeth are as sharp as a thorn.

**Zara Sethi (7)**
Loxford School, Ilford

# Naughty Bulldog

He's a big, bad beast
Who lives in the east
He eats big tins
From great big bins
With his great big teeth
He's a bulldog with a great big butt
He's a great big beast
He's a security bulldog
And likes a lot of purity.

**Riam Parekh (9)**
Loxford School, Ilford

# Ghost Spirit

The ghost is gone,
The ghost is a spirit,
The ghost is evil,
The ghost is violent,
The ghost is a villain,
The ghost is like a demon,
The ghost is a part of you,
The spirit is there,
The spirit is here,
The spirit is you.

**Mathu Shalini (7)**
Loxford School, Ilford

# Never Come Out At Midnight

Midnight is as fast as Flash
Midnight sparkles with the stars
In the beautiful sky
Midnight is as horrid as a teacher
Monsters come out and scare children
And make babies cry
Midnight was as handsome as you have ever seen.

## Mysha Miah (8)
Loxford School, Ilford

# My Creepy Monster Sannar

My monster's name is Sannar
He is usually pale but is now tanned
He bites with his big teeth
He would stick to you like a leech
His heart is made of ice
Be careful, he has lice!

**Roshan Jeyakumar (7)**
Loxford School, Ilford

# Tree Monster

There was a monster
His body had a green colour
In winter he changed to brown
And he went down to the ground
He always wanted to be a tree
So that he could be free!

## Mihran Khan (8)
Loxford School, Ilford

# Terror-Striking Ripcon

I feel the darkness, the fangs of a monster
I sense it is getting stronger
It is not long before he comes
For his name means dangerous and it is Ripcon.

**Zwabit Intesaar Hamid (8)**
Loxford School, Ilford

# The Naminator

When you're walking down the stream,
Remember not to dream,
You drift off into a dream land,
But a monster is lurking around,
The Naminator!
You don't know how to talk or walk and you see,
A tree full of Naminators!
There's one on your back,
You're lucky it's just a dream!
You wake up,
It's *not* a dream!
It's slimy and whiny,
And not very shiny,
It's bland and it's got its own land,
Called Nightmare Land!
Naminator...
If you have a shiny thing, hide it!
For a glistening monster,
As quiet as a mouse,
Lurks around under the shadows.

I have a necklace,
It has pearls and emeralds.
A Naminator with an eye for shiny things
Grabs my hand,
It uses its claws to snatch my precious necklace
Out of my pampered hands,
I scream loudly and the stream rapidly rampages.
The Naminator climbs up a tree,
And disappears,
I walk back home,
My mom asks: "Where's your necklace?"
I hesitated and said, "An animal stole if from me."
I never have seen another Naminator,
But I know there are some hiding somewhere...

**Tomisin Hannora Joel (8)**
Salisbury Cathedral School, Salisbury

# The Red Suffer

The woods were dark
As dark as night
Even though it was light
The trees rattled
The wind whistled
But I knew I wasn't alone
A white blur shot past me
I bumped into a tree
And spun around
There were claw marks all up the tree
As deep as a puddle
And then I saw it
As silver as metal
Red ooze dripping down its back
I tried to run but I was frozen with fear
Suddenly, it turned around
I saw it, it saw me
We were face-to-face
I knew what it was
It was the Red Suffer
I thought it was a myth

It said in a deep voice, "Can I have a peppermint
To suck? I've had a sore throat for years."
And so I gave him a peppermint
He cleared his throat and said
In a jolly voice,
"There's a party inside me, literally!"
Then he swallowed me whole
He was right
There was a massive disco inside him.

**Bertie Barrington (8)**
Salisbury Cathedral School, Salisbury

# The Ten-Eyed Bob

The Ten-Eyed Bob came down to Earth
Chomping chewed up toffee and turf
Down came the monster, stiff and bold
To steal told stories
*Whoosh!* And down he came
To steal told stories
Stealthy, sloppy, stomping through the door
Up the stairs
And down the winding corridor
"Fe, fi, fo, fum, I am the monster and here I come."
I see the slimy hand through the door
Through the little blueberries door
I screamed out loud to wake my mum
But the leg of the bed just fell down
The bed, as thin as a leg, came down to Bob
And *squish!*
It squashes him down and green slime oozed out
The Ten-Eyed Bob was now beaten but later eaten!

## Jasper Sainsbury (9)
Salisbury Cathedral School, Salisbury

# Fluffball The Lightning Catcher

Fluffy by name but not by nature
Pink as a marshmallow, fluffy as candy
But lightning feet planting traps
Well, she walks through the woods
For all the children
So she has some friends
But she plants strawberry trees everywhere
But very, very quietly
But suddenly, it went *boom!*
The traps went off
The trees are whistling and rattling
But she climbed the tree because
She thought she would be protected
Then she fell down, down, down
And *splash!*
She fell into a puddle!
She got so wet on her fluffy fur
I was so heavy that she couldn't walk
Until it was dry.

## Honour Veitch (8)
Salisbury Cathedral School, Salisbury

# Monster Time

I can hear a squeak coming from under the bed
Is it the springs?
No
I see a paw
I sit on my bed and am so busy
Worrying
I don't see a leg until
It's the whole leg
A monster comes out from under my bed
Small as a mouse
Fluffy as falling snow
Cute as a newborn pup
Crawling onto my bed
She tells me her name
"Fluffballpip," she says
"Well," I say
But before I can say something else
She takes me away
Into the dark night, we fly
Suddenly, *splash!* We fall into the sea

Soon I see dolphins
"They are all mine," she announces
At once, I knew she was good.

**Allegra Sturgeon (8)**
Salisbury Cathedral School, Salisbury

# The Space Monster

Before you go to space, my son,
Do not go tomorrow,
There is a space monster lurking,
Its name is Kafung.
When you were young
You believed in aliens
But now they're real!
But why am I talking about aliens, you say?
Because every one billion years, aliens invade!
But the space monster protects Earth,
And uses the aliens' slimy eyeballs as breath mints!
Sorry to scare you, it's all true!
But don't worry about the aliens,
They only invade for a day.
Oh! I forgot about the space monster,
It's so friendly to humans!
It makes its appearance as a cheeky, fluffy
monster!

**Tofunmi Joel (8)**
Salisbury Cathedral School, Salisbury

# A Little Surprise

I hear my door creak
I think there is something
In my cupboard
It opens completely
I see a little water dragon
"Hello," I say
"Hello," it replies
"My name is Pipskweek,
I'm a water dragon."
"My name is little Lilly."
"I'm very fluffy and I'm
Good at flying
Come on, let's go on an adventure."
"Let me put on my boots, wait a minute."
We fly around the world
And get home in the morning
I ask if I can keep Pipskweek.
"Yes!"

**Emily Luton (9)**
Salisbury Cathedral School, Salisbury

# The Blob Monster

You can hear the slime dropping off his gooey
body
As each drop glows in the dark
At first, your bedroom door opens with a creak
As loud as wood being chopped off a tree
Then the next moment, you're slimy and soaking
By the breath of Goodrop
You can taste the breath of him
You can see the goo on his invisible tongue
But then he turns on your bedside light
And reads you a bedtime story
He goes to sleep with you
And when you wake up
There is a cuddly toy called Goodrop
Who was sleeping there with you!

**Safiya Laycock-Wright (9)**
Salisbury Cathedral School, Salisbury

# What's That In The Darkness?

What's that in the darkness?
Something big and hairy
Come to eat my toys and clothes
And I think it's very scary
What's that in the darkness?
Something fat and smelly
Come to take my friends away
And it wobbles like a jelly
What's that in the darkness?
Something tall and stupid
Comes to chew my toothbrush
Which is not cool for a Cupid
What's that in the darkness?
It gave me such a fright
I reached to turn the light on
But it was only Mum
Come to kiss me goodnight!

**Beth Sainsbury (9)**
Salisbury Cathedral School, Salisbury

# The Slayer

On Monday night, a deadly monster
Called The Slayer came rumbling down the street
If he sees you, run away!
He loves to eat human mums, dads, the lot
He likes cats the most
He is hard to spot because he is
As black as night
But that is not the end
He can smell your fear
He tracks you down to the very last night
He eats your flesh and grinds your bones to dust
And puts it in a pot of his favourite food
So if you see him, run away
Or you will be trapped between his jaws.

## Robert Wallace (9)

Salisbury Cathedral School, Salisbury

# Death-Bone

I can hear the whoosh of wind
Rustling all the bins
He plunders through the darkest nights
Taking too many huge bites
He'll eat your feet when you're asleep
Don't you dare make a peep
I can smell some rotten cheese
And feel the lump under my bed
He doesn't walk, he has no feet
Instead, he'll glide with heat
But when I see a monster
As blue as the sea
It shall be my monster
So I know not to be afraid.

**Amelia Parker (8)**
Salisbury Cathedral School, Salisbury

# What's That?

He's short, deadly and blue
He's even slimy too
His horns are as sharp as a knife
And he is as grumpy as Simon Cowell

He's short, deadly and blue
He's even slimy too
He's got sticky, green hands and feet
He even smells like a garbage bin

He's short, deadly and blue
He's even slimy too
His teeth are like daggers
They can kill you in one touch
Oh! It's the short but deadly wart.

**Noah Maguire (8)**
Salisbury Cathedral School, Salisbury

# The Evil Gloomy George

Gloomy George lurks in the corner of your room
And he comes to creep and gloom
Uh-oh, where is he?
I can hear growls under my bed...
Aaargh!

The monster tells me his name is George
Gloomy George
He takes me into the garden
"Give me some chocolate, or I'll gobble you up."
Poor me gets gobbled up.
I got through the oesophagus
Then disgusting digestion
And not a pleasant journey!

**Henry Seaward Gower (8)**
Salisbury Cathedral School, Salisbury

# The Middle Of The Night

It is the middle of the night
"Growl!"
Two red eyes glimmer and move around
*Snuffle!*
Something touches me, soft and furry
*Purr!*
A chlorine smell drifts over me
*Hiccup!*
Something slippery slides over my legs
*Slither*
Hot horse-like breath fills my nostrils
*Gurgle*
Something warm cuddles me
Flipper Warty, my lovely toy monster.

**Rachel Fisher (8)**
Salisbury Cathedral School, Salisbury

# Miniature Fluff

The roars, the shining jaws,
Down the bumpy street,
Through the forest,
It gets louder, louder and louder
I knew what it was
It suddenly stopped and out of the gloom
A face popped up
A white and fluffy face
That looked familiar
From the book of monsters
She politely came out and said
Her name was Miniature Fluff
But she took one look and me
And I was gone.

**Jessica Merrick (8)**
Salisbury Cathedral School, Salisbury

# Pop

A pop
Is a monster
So they say
It's the only thing
That lives
By the bay
The pop is
Very big
Long and
Scary
And it has terrible
Wind
*Bang, crash, clink*
Down it came
A monster...
In Pompeii
I ran and ran
Until I was far
Then I sat
By a cosy fire
The fire was as red as blood

Suddenly
Stop
I heard a
Pop.

## William Wallace (9)
Salisbury Cathedral School, Salisbury

# Abominable Wolf!

One snowy day, I was playing in the snow,
When the moon was about to glow;
In the distance, I could see,
A very white thing coming to me;

When it was there, it was most fluffy,
And also super chilly;
It was cold all over,
And it nearly had an antenna;

When winter fell down,
We all made a big frown;
And when I had to say goodbye,
Spring was passing by.

**Mollie Johnson (8)**
Salisbury Cathedral School, Salisbury

# In The Fruit Bowl

What's that in the fruit bowl?
It's curved and comical
But deadly, what is it?

It's a banana dragon!
Run!
Mmm, yum!
Oh no, here comes the kiwi dragon,
Aaargh!

"Don't be scared,
I'm not mean," said the dragon
"I'll give you fruits and snacks."
We've been friends ever since.

## George Gostik (8)
Salisbury Cathedral School, Salisbury

# Will The Mid Wing Shadow

Suddenly, I woke up
In the moonlight shadow, something moved
Bright, light green like
Spring leaves, emerald-shaped wings
Flapping about all over the place
Teeth like sharp, shiny diamonds
Dimming in the darkness.

**Ben Gregory (8)**
Salisbury Cathedral School, Salisbury

# Blue Blob

Blob is wriggling slime
All of the time
Blob is as blue as a jellyfish I knew
Although he is quite sweet
He doesn't have any feet
Blob sleeps under my bed
And guess what?
My name is... Fred!

**Jonti Michael Drummond Simpson (8)**
Salisbury Cathedral School, Salisbury

# The Teeth Nicker Monster!

Something crept from under my bed
I could see something red seeping
From under my bed
I could see orange horns
The size of a lamp post
I could see bright, blue eyes
Looking at me
Not taking his eyes off me
Fred the pink-furred monster
Crept from under my bed
He waited, then he went and took
All the children's teeth
He got his super, superglue out
And glued all the teeth into his mouth
Fred went back under the bed
To his monster world
And fell asleep on his monster bed!

**Tillie Louise Gardener (10)**
Teignmouth Community School, Teignmouth

# Altya The Monster

Altya the monster was one day flying in the woods,
But she couldn't fly very well
And found herself doing everything backwards
She has a small, round body
With purple, spotty fur
A little boy stepped on her tail
And she went, "Purr!"
When she gets super-duper angry
Red spikes pop out from her back
So when the little boy stood up
She gave him a whack!
Never, ever make Altya angry, otherwise...
She'll go mental and eat you in her pies.

**Sophia Dalling (7)**
Teignmouth Community School, Teignmouth

# Deep, Dark Night

I went to bed at deep, dark night
And dreamt of a knight
Coming to save me
The wind blew like usual
In the old town
But the floorboards creaked
This wasn't usual
Something was under my bed
Just then, she came out
Looked at me
And started to sing a song:
'I'm very green,
Just like a green bean
My spots are pink
And I like to wink!
I won't hurt a fly
Which is zooming through the sky!'
And we became friends.

## Grace Swift (10)
Teignmouth Community School, Teignmouth

# Box

I have a monster in my house
He is so small, like a mouse
He lives in my wardrobe and comes out at night
He has an antenna on his head that shines like a
light
I had new trainers just last week
Which he loves to put on his feet
He wore them at night, then he jumped on my bed
But when I woke up, he went to bed
I called him Box as he lives in my old shoebox
As his home.

## Laila Auckland Edwards (7)
Teignmouth Community School, Teignmouth

YoungWriters
Est. 1991

# Detective Uni Flame The Dino That Lives Outside

It was night
I heard a bang from the garden
He's short
He has long fangs
He can shape-shift into a Pokémon
There was a note on the floor
It said, 'Beware, don't step foot on the floor'.
He sneaks through the night
But I still can't see him.

## Alfie Morley (7)
Teignmouth Community School, Teignmouth

# YOUNG WRITERS INFORMATION

We hope you have enjoyed reading this book – and that you will continue to in the coming years.

If you're a young writer who enjoys reading and creative writing, or the parent of an enthusiastic poet or story writer, do visit our website **www.youngwriters.co.uk**. Here you will find free competitions, workshops and games, as well as recommended reads, a poetry glossary and our blog. There's lots to keep budding writers motivated to write!

If you would like to order further copies of this book, or any of our other titles, then please give us a call or order via your online account.

Young Writers
Remus House
Coltsfoot Drive
Peterborough
PE2 9BF
(01733) 890066
**info@youngwriters.co.uk**

Join in the conversation!
Tips, news, giveaways and much more!

 **YoungWritersUK**       **@YoungWritersCW**